Graphic Chillers

DR. & MR. JEKYLL HYDE

ADAPTED AND ILLUSTRATED BY

JASON HO

BASED UPON THE WORKS OF

ROBERT LOUIS STEVENSON

EDGE
FRANKLIN WATTS

LONDON·SYDNEY

DR. & MR. JEKYLL HYDE

ABOUT THE AUTHOR

Robert Louis Stevenson was born on 13 November 1850, in Edinburgh, Scotland. He was the only son of Thomas Stevenson and Margaret Isabella Balfour.

At 17, Stevenson entered Edinburgh University, where he was supposed to study engineering. Instead, he began to study law. In 1875, Stevenson was called to the Scottish bar, but never practised.

He travelled often and found a lot to write about. Slowly, his writing career developed. His travel stories first appeared in magazines and later in novels. They grew in popularity and he later became well known.

In 1880, Stevenson married American Fanny Vandegrift Osbourne. He continued to travel with his wife and stepson, Lloyd Osbourne. He visited America, the South Pacific and Samoa.

The Stevensons settled in Samoa in 1890. The climate there was good for Stevenson's health. He was very active until he died suddenly on 3 December 1894. Today, Robert Louis Stevenson is best known for his novels of adventure and suspense.

"IT WAS ABOUT THREE O'CLOCK ON A *BLACK* MORNING, AND I WAS ON MY WAY HOME. I SAW A LITTLE MAN STRUTTING ALONG, AND A GIRL ABOUT TEN YEARS OLD RUNNING FROM THE STREET. THEY RAN INTO EACH OTHER. BUT THE *FIENDISH* THING IS, THE MAN CALMLY *TRAMPLED* OVER THE CHILD, LEAVING HER *SCREAMING* ON THE GROUND."

"I *SHOUTED* AT THE MAN, *CHASED* HIM AND *GRABBED* HIM. HE DID NOT RESIST, BUT GAVE ME SUCH AN *UGLY* GLARE IT BROUGHT ME OUT IN A SWEAT."

OOOOOFF!

"THE CHILD WAS TREATED BY THE DOCTOR, WHOM SHE WAS ORIGINALLY LOOKING FOR. I ATTEMPTED TO KEEP THE MOTHER AWAY FROM THE LITTLE MAN."

"IT WAS AGREED THAT THE MAN WOULD APOLOGISE WITH A *PAYMENT* TO THE MOTHER. AT THAT POINT WE WERE LED TO THAT VERY DOOR. HE BROUGHT OUT TEN POUNDS IN *GOLD* AND A *CHEQUE*."

"I WAS SURE THAT THE *CHEQUE* WAS A *FORGERY*, BUT WAS ASSURED THAT IT WAS GENUINE."

"THEN MR. UTTERSON ASKED THE NAME OF THE MAN WHO WALKED OVER THE GIRL. 'HE WAS CALLED HYDE,' SAID MR. ENFIELD. 'WHAT DID HE LOOK LIKE?' ASKED MR. UTTERSON."

"HE IS NOT EASY TO DESCRIBE. THERE WAS SOMETHING *BITTER* AND *TWISTED* ABOUT HIM. I NEVER MET A MAN I SO DISLIKED, YET I'M UNSURE AS TO WHY."

"THAT VERY NIGHT, UTTERSON WENT INTO HIS STUDY AND GOT A DOCUMENT FROM HIS SAFE. IT WAS ENDORSED AS DR. JEKYLL'S WILL. THE WILL SAID THAT UPON HENRY JEKYLL'S DEATH OR DISAPPEARANCE, HIS POSSESIONS WERE TO BE PASSED TO EDWARD HYDE."

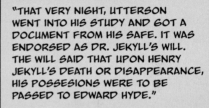

"UTTERSON WONDERED IF THIS COULD BE THE SAME MAN WHO TRAMPLED THE GIRL IN THE STREET. HE ASKED AN OLD FRIEND, DR. LANYON, FOR HELP. THEY HAD BOTH BEEN FRIENDS OF HENRY JEKYLL SOME TIME AGO."

"WHEN UTTERSON ASKED ABOUT EDWARD HYDE, LANYON REPLIED:"

HYDE? NO, I'VE NEVER HEARD OF HIM.

"FROM THAT MOMENT ON, UTTERSON BEGAN TO WATCH THE DOORWAY OF THAT *WRETCHED* PLACE. IN THE MORNINGS, DURING THE AFTERNOON AND WELL INTO THE EVENING, UNTIL FINALLY..."

MR. HYDE, I THINK?

THAT IS MY NAME, WHAT DO YOU WANT?

"UTTERSON INTRODUCED HIMSELF. HE MENTIONED THAT DR. JEKYLL WAS AN OLD FRIEND WHO HAD TOLD HIM OF HIS FRIEND HYDE. TO WHICH HYDE RESPONDED WITH..."

RUBBISH! HE NEVER TOLD YOU - YOU'RE A LIAR.

THERE'S NO NEED TO BE RUDE, SIR.

"AT THIS, HYDE BELLOWED A *HORRIBLE LAUGH*, THEN HE QUICKLY DISAPPEARED THROUGH THE DOORWAY."

"UTTERSON WALKED AROUND THE CORNER TO A TIDIER STREET. THERE HE CAME TO DR. JEKYLL'S DOOR."

"UTTERSON KNOCKED AND MR. POOLE ANSWERED THE DOOR. INSIDE, UTTERSON ASKED IF DR. JEKYLL WAS IN AND IF POOLE KNEW ANYTHING ABOUT MR. HYDE. POOLE HAD NOT SEEN DR. JEKYLL, OR HEARD OF MR. HYDE."

"A FEW NIGHTS LATER, A DINNER PARTY WAS HELD AT THE HOME OF HENRY JEKYLL. SEVERAL OF HIS CLOSEST FRIENDS ATTENDED – MR. UTTERSON WAS ONE OF THEM."

"IT WAS NOT UNCOMMON FOR UTTERSON TO STAY LONG AFTER THE OTHER GUESTS LEFT. BUT THAT NIGHT, HE HAD A *SUBJECT OF INTEREST* TO DISCUSS WITH JEKYLL."

"A VERY PLEASANT EVENING BECAME *CLOUDED* WITH TALK OF JEKYLL'S WILL. UTTERSON INSISTED THAT SUCH A DOCUMENT WAS *STRANGE*. HE MENTIONED THE ENCOUNTER WITH HYDE, WHICH MADE DR. JEKYLL GROW PALE WITH ANXIETY."

VERY WELL, I PROMISE.

I KNOW YOU HAVE SEEN HIM, HE TOLD ME SO. I ALSO KNOW HE WAS RUDE, BUT I TAKE A *GREAT INTEREST* IN MR. HYDE. IF I AM TAKEN AWAY, PROMISE THAT YOU'LL BEAR WITH HIM, AND CARRY OUT THE LAST REQUEST IN MY WILL.

"NEARLY A YEAR LATER, AN *UNSPEAKABLE CRIME* OCCURRED, AND WAS MADE MORE *TERRIFYING* BY THE MANNER OF THE ATTACK. A YOUNG WOMAN AT A WINDOW SAW A MAN APPROACH ANOTHER MAN ON THE STREET. THE PLEASANT-LOOKING INDIVIDUAL BEGAN SPEAKING TO THE OTHER, WHO WITHOUT WARNING BEGAN TO *BEAT HIM TO DEATH* WITH A CANE."

"WHEN THE SCENE WAS EXAMINED, NOTHING WAS FOUND EXCEPT HALF A PIECE OF A BROKEN CANE AND A LETTER ADDRESSED TO MR. UTTERSON."

NO!

"THE NEXT MORNING, THE POLICE BROUGHT THE LETTER AND PART OF A WALKING CANE TO MR. UTTERSON. UTTERSON IMMEDIATELY RECOGNISED THE HALF OF CANE AS ONE HE HAD GIVEN AS A GIFT TO DR. JEKYLL."

"BOTH THE INSPECTOR AND MR. UTTERSON WENT TO SEE MR. EDWARD HYDE. WHEN THE HOUSEKEEPER LET THEM IN, THEY FOUND HIS ROOM HAD BEEN *RANSACKED*. IT WAS THERE THAT THE INSPECTOR DISCOVERED THE OTHER HALF OF THE CANE."

"THE NEXT AFTERNOON, UTTERSON WENT TO JEKYLL'S PRIVATE ROOM."

"THERE, UTTERSON FOUND DR. JEKYLL IN A *TERRIBLE CONDITION*. IT WAS AT THIS POINT THAT JEKYLL PRODUCED A LETTER IN HYDE'S OWN HAND. IT STATED HYDE'S INTENTION TO ESCAPE. IT WAS A RELIEF TO UTTERSON TO KNOW THAT JEKYLL WOULD HAVE NO MORE TO DO WITH THAT MAN."

"LATER THAT EVENING, UTTERSON FELT EXHAUSTED. WITH HIM WAS HIS HEAD CLERK, MR. GUEST, WHO WAS AWARE OF THE CURRENT SITUATION. GUEST WAS ALSO A STUDENT AND CRITIC OF HANDWRITING. IT WAS HIS KNOWLEDGE OF HANDWRITING THAT UTTERSON NEEDED."

"JUST THEN, THE MAID ENTERED WITH A DINNER INVITATION FROM DR. JEKYLL. MR. GUEST THEN COMPARED JEKYLL'S NOTE TO THAT OF HYDE'S."

"MR. GUEST FOUND A CURIOUS THING ABOUT BOTH NOTES. THEY WERE WRITTEN BY THE *SAME PERSON*."

"TIME WENT ON AND THE SEARCH FOR HYDE HAD ALMOST STOPPED. DURING THIS TIME, JEKYLL HAD ONCE AGAIN BEGUN TO HAVE GUESTS AND TO BE FULL OF LIFE AGAIN."

"ONE EVENING, UTTERSON AND LANYON WERE INVITED TO DINNER AT DR. JEKYLL'S HOME. THE THREE WERE VERY FRIENDLY – AS IF NOTHING TERRIBLE HAD EVER HAPPENED."

"THE NEXT DAY, UTTERSON TRIED TO VISIT JEKYLL'S HOME, BUT HE WAS NOT ALLOWED IN."

"A FEW DAYS LATER IT WAS THE SAME. FINALLY, UTTERSON DECIDED TO VISIT DR. LANYON."

"WHAT HE FOUND WAS *DISTURBING.* LANYON WAS IN A *DEATHLY STATE.* HE HAD WITHERED AWAY AND DIDN'T LOOK WELL."

I HAVE HAD A *SHOCK* THAT I'LL NEVER RECOVER FROM.

JEKYLL IS ILL TOO. HAVE YOU BEEN ABLE TO SEE HIM?

I DON'T WANT TO SEE OR HEAR OF HIM AGAIN.

DON'T *EVER* SPEAK OF HIM AGAIN.

"A WEEK LATER, LANYON WAS *DEAD.* UTTERSON RECEIVED A LETTER FROM LANYON, HEADED: 'PRIVATE, FOR THE HAND OF G.J. UTTERSON ALONE, IN THE CASE OF HIS DEATH, TO BE DESTROYED UNREAD'."

"UTTERSON WAS CURIOUS, BUT HE RESPECTED THE WISHES OF HIS FRIEND. HE PLACED THE LETTER IN HIS SAFE, UNOPENED."

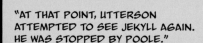

"AT THAT POINT, UTTERSON ATTEMPTED TO SEE JEKYLL AGAIN. HE WAS STOPPED BY POOLE."

"THEN, ON ANOTHER SUNDAY, MR. ENFIELD AND MR. UTTERSON WALKED THROUGH TOWN TOWARDS DR. JEKYLL'S HOUSE..."

"UTTERSON OPENED THE ENVELOPE ONLY TO FIND ANOTHER SEALED ENVELOPE. ON IT WAS WRITTEN: 'NOT TO BE OPENED UNTIL THE DEATH OR DISAPPEARANCE OF DR. HENRY JEKYLL'."

"SOME DAYS LATER, UTTERSON WAS RELAXING AFTER DINNER, WHEN POOLE ENTERED WITH A CONCERNED LOOK ON HIS FACE."

I HAVE BEEN WORRED FOR A WEEK ABOUT DR. JEKYLL'S CONDITION, BUT NOW SOMETHING IS VERY WRONG. YOU MUST COME AND SEE FOR YOURSELF, SIR.

"UTTERSON GRABBED HIS COAT AND LEFT WITH POOLE INTO THE NIGHT. WHEN THEY ENTERED THE HOME OF DR. JEKYLL, HIS SERVANTS WERE ALL TOGETHER – SCARED AND AFRAID."

AND NOW, MR. UTTERSON, WALK WITH ME AS QUIETLY AS YOU CAN.

"THEY MADE THEIR WAY THROUGH THE COURTYARD AND INTO THE SURGICAL THEATRE, AND THEN TO THE STEPS OF JEKYLL'S PRIVATE ROOM."

SIR, MR. UTTERSON IS HERE TO SEE YOU.

TELL HIM I CANNOT SEE ANYONE.

"POOLE HAD BEEN EMPLOYED BY DR. JEKYLL FOR WELL OVER 20 YEARS – HE WAS SURE HE KNEW HIS OWN MASTER'S VOICE. AND THAT VOICE FROM BEHIND THE DOOR WAS NOT IT."

THAT VOICE FROM INSIDE HAS BEEN CRYING FOR SOME SORT OF MEDICINE ALL WEEK.

I WAS GIVEN LISTS OF THINGS TO GET FROM CHEMISTS IN TOWN. BUT EVERY TIME I COME BACK WITH IT ALL, HE SAYS IT IS IMPURE OR BAD QUALITY.

"POOLE HACKED AT THE DOOR UNTIL IT GAVE IN."

"THERE, ON THE FLOOR, LAY A BODY STILL TWITCHING. IT WAS NOT DR. JEKYLL, BUT EDWARD HYDE. NEXT TO HIM LAY A CRUSHED GLASS WHICH HAD CONTAINED SOME SORT OF VILE LIQUID."

"THEY SEARCHED EVERYWHERE FOR JEKYLL."

"BUT THEY COULDN'T FIND HIM ANYWHERE."

"THEY THOUGHT HE MAY HAVE FLED."

"BUT THE RUSTED KEY THAT OPENED THE REAR ENTRANCE HAD BEEN BROKEN."

"LATER, THEY RE-ENTERED JEKYLL'S PRIVATE ROOM. THEY DISCOVERED SOME DOCUMENTS WHICH WERE DATED THAT DAY. THEY ALSO FOUND LETTERS ADDRESSED TO UTTERSON."

PLEASE DON'T TELL ANYONE ABOUT THIS. IF DR. JEKYLL HAS FLED OR IS DEAD, AT LEAST WE CAN SAVE HIS REPUTATION.

I'M HEADING HOME TO LOOK AT WHAT WE'VE FOUND. I WILL CALL THE POLICE LATER.

"BOTH ARRIVED JUST AFTER I DID."

"THEY STARTED TO WORK AWAY AT THE DOOR."

"FINALLY, BOTH THE DOOR AND CABINET WERE OPENED. I TOOK THE ITEMS I NEEDED AND LEFT."

"INSIDE THE BOX, I FOUND A WRAPPER OF SOME SALT-LIKE SUBSTANCE, AND A BOTTLE OF RED LIQUID, WHICH HAD A VERY STRONG, UNPLEASANT SMELL..."

"THERE WAS ALSO A JOURNAL WITH ENTRIES DATING BACK SEVERAL YEARS. PEPPERED HERE AND THERE WERE ADDITIONS TO SOME OF THE ENTRIES, SAYING '*DOUBLE*' AND IN SOME INSTANCE, '*TOTAL FAILURE*'."

"I BEGAN TO WONDER WHAT ALL THIS MEANT. I WOULD HAVE TO WAIT A FEW MORE HOURS TO FIND THAT OUT..."

"I DIDN'T UNDERSTAND WHY THESE THINGS WERE SO IMPORTANT. BUT TO BE CAUTIOUS, I LOADED MY *REVOLVER* JUST IN CASE."

"THE CLOCK CHIMED MIDNIGHT, WHEN THERE WAS A FAINT KNOCK AT THE DOOR."

ARE YOU THE FRIEND OF DR. JEKYLL'S?

YES.

"I INVITED HIM IN. BEFORE DOING SO HE LOOKED BACK AS IF SURE HE WAS BEING FOLLOWED. THIS MADE ME ANXIOUS AND I THOUGHT ABOUT THE REVOLVER IN MY POCKET."

"AFTER A FEW STEPS INSIDE MY HOME, A *FIRE* LIT WITHIN HIS EYES AS HE SAID:"

COME SIR, I DON'T EVEN KNOW WHO YOU ARE. PLEASE, WON'T YOU TAKE A SEAT?

DO YOU HAVE IT? DID YOU BRING IT HERE?

I APOLOGISE. PLEASE FORGIVE MY RUDENESS.

17

"UTTERSON MOVED ON TO DR. JEKYLL'S JOURNAL, FILLED WITH FEAR AS TO WHAT HE MIGHT FIND IN ITS PAGES..."

"I KNOW NOW THAT WHAT I HAD DONE WAS *HORRIBLE*. BUT MY INTEREST IN SEPARATING THE *GOOD* FROM THE *EVIL* WAS TOO GREAT."

"IT WAS MY SINCERE DESIRE TO BE ABLE TO *SPLIT* THE MAN THAT WAS EVIL FROM THE MAN THAT WAS GOOD. SO THAT THEY COULD LEAD TWO DIFFERENT LIVES WITHOUT INFLUENCING EACH OTHER."

GACK!

"WHEN I REACHED THE POINT WHERE IT WAS TIME TO TEST THE THEORY, I DECIDE TO TEST IT ON *MYSELF*."

"IT WAS WHEN I WAS CONSTANTLY FIGHTING THE URGE TO LET HYDE LOOSE THAT I WAS PARTNER TO A CRIME. IT WAS NOT SO *TERRIBLE*, AS IT WAS *CRUEL*."

owwwww!

CLUMP!

"TWO MONTHS BEFORE THE *MURDER* OF THAT POOR MAN, I HAD COME HOME FROM A NIGHT OF ADVENTURE AS MR. HYDE. BUT I FOUND MYSELF NOT IN HYDE'S ROOM, BUT IN MY OWN BEDROOM."

"I COULDN'T UNDERSTAND HOW IT HAD HAPPENED. I HAD TO GET TO THE LABORATORY BEFORE ANYONE SAW ME LIKE THAT."

"I DRESSED AS WELL AS I COULD AND HEADED TOWARDS THE LABORATORY. UNFORTUNATELY, POOLE SAW ME RUNNING ABOUT BEFORE I COULD MAKE IT OUTSIDE."

"HOWEVER, I MADE IT TO MY PRIVATE ROOM SAFELY. I MIXED SOME OF THE DRINK, WHICH CHANGED ME INTO MY NORMAL SELF."

"I WAS *DISTRAUGHT* AT THE THOUGHT OF TRANSFORMING WITHOUT WARNING. IT WAS AS IF HYDE WANTED TO COME OUT ON HIS OWN, AND FOR TWO MONTHS I *RESTRAINED* MYSELF FROM DRINKING THE POTION. I HOPED TO PREVENT ANY SORT OF TROUBLE THAT HYDE WOULD CAUSE."

"BUT AS TIME WENT ON, I FORGOT ABOUT THE *CONSEQUENCES* OF DRINKING SUCH A LIQUID."

"I COULDN'T BE CONTAINED. THE SHEER *DELIGHT* OF BEING HYDE WAS TOO MUCH. I RELISHED EVERY MINUTE OF BEING *EVIL*."

AIIIIEEEEE - STOP!

"I CAME BACK TO MYSELF AFTER DRINKING THE POTION. I WAS THANKFUL THAT IT WAS OVER. THE *GUILT* WITHIN ME WAS STRONG AND I PROMISED MYSELF THAT I WOULD NEVER DRINK IT AGAIN."

"LOOKING BACK, I REMEMBER HOW *DEVIOUS* HYDE HAD BECOME. AFTER COMMITTING AN ACT OF MURDER, HE BEGAN BURNING ANY AND ALL PAPERS THAT WOULD CONNECT HIM AND HIS TERRIBLE CRIME."

"AT THAT POINT, I MADE A DECISION TO STEP BACK INTO THE WORLD OF MAN AND JOIN MY FRIENDS AS DR. HENRY JEKYLL."

"THAT *FATEFUL DAY* CAME WHEN I WAS OUT ENJOYING THE WORLD AS I HAD BEFORE MY DISCOVERY OF HYDE."

"THE CHANGE CAME *SUDDENLY.* I COULD FEEL IT RUNNING THROUGHOUT MY BODY."

AAAAAAAAAAA!

"I TOLD MYSELF I COULDN'T BE SEEN LIKE THIS. I REARRANGED MY CLOTHES AS BEST I COULD..."

"I CAUGHT A CAB. I HAD TO GET MYSELF INDOORS AS QUICKLY AS POSSIBLE."

"MY CAB STOPPED IN FRONT OF AN INN, AND WHEN I GOT OUT, THE DRIVER *LAUGHED* AT MY FACE."

ACK!

"I CAN'T BE SURE OF WHAT I DID. BUT I KNOW THAT THE DRIVER WAS *BADLY HURT.*"

"AT THE INN, I SHOWED SUCH AN UGLY FACE THAT IT *SCARED* THE SERVANTS."

"THE ATTENDANT THAT TOOK THE LETTERS TO BE SENT OFF TO DR. LANYON AND POOLE, WAS ALSO AFRAID TO LOOK AT ME."

"AFTER THAT, I SAT IN THE ROOM WAITING FOR TIME TO GO BY. EVENTUALLY, I TOOK ANOTHER CAB IN ORDER TO GET TO DR. LANYON'S HOME."

"AS I GOT OUT OF THE CAB, I WAS APPROACHED BY A STREET SELLER."

"THE *ANGER* INSIDE OF HYDE CAME OUT IN ONE SWIFT BLOW."

CRACK!

AGH!

"WHEN I CAME ROUND AT LANYON'S, I WAS CONCERNED AT HIS POOR CONDITION."

"LANYON WAS *DISGUSTED* AND *APPALLED* AT THE SIGHT OF ME..."

"HE BEGAN TO *SCREAM.* WHAT HE SAID I DON'T REALLY KNOW, BUT I LEFT TIRED AND NOT MY REGULAR SELF."

"BUT I COULD FEEL HYDE TRYING TO COME OUT. THE THOUGHT OF THIS MADE ME BOTH *PHYSICALLY* AND *MENTALLY* SICK."

"EVENTUALLY IT WORE OFF AND HYDE *REAPPEARED*."

"A WEEK HAD PASSED AND I WAS DOWN TO A SMALL AMOUNT OF SALTS NEEDED TO STOP THE CHANGE. POOLE WAS SENT TO FETCH ME MORE OF THE SALTS..."

"BUT NONE OF THE NEW SUPPLY WOULD WORK."

"I BELIEVE THAT THE SUPPLY I HAD ORIGINALLY BOUGHT WAS SOMEHOW *NOT PURE.* IT IS THIS DIFFERENCE THAT HAD TURNED ME INTO WHAT I AM NOW. I DON'T KNOW WHAT IT IS OR HOW MUCH OF A DIFFERENCE IT TAKES TO MAKES ME CHANGE."

This edition first published in 2010 by
Franklin Watts
338 Euston Road
London NW1 3BH

Franklin Watts Australia
Level 17/207 Kent Street
Sydney NSW 2000

First published in the USA by Magic Wagon, a division of the ABDO Group

1 3 5 7 9 10 8 6 4 2

Based upon the works of Robert Louis Stevenson
Adapted and illustrated by Jason Ho
Letters and colours by Jay Fotos
Edited and directed by Chazz DeMoss
Cover design by Neil Klinepier
UK cover design by Peter Scoulding

A CIP catalogue record for this book is available from the British Library.

Dewey number: 741.5

ISBN: 978 0 7496 9686 3

Printed in China

Franklin Watts is a division of Hachette Children's Books,
an Hachette UK company.
www.hachette.co.uk

Graphic Chillers Sneak peek...

THE ENTIRE VILLAGE BELIEVES IN *GHOST STORIES* AND LOCAL TALES OF HAUNTED AREAS.

WHEN THE INKY BLACKNESS OF NIGHT COVERS SLEEPY HOLLOW, IT IS BELIEVED THAT MANY *TORMENTED SPECTRES* AND *MOURNFUL GHOSTS* ARISE. THEY LEAVE THEIR HAUNTED SPACES TO ADD THEIR SUPERNATURAL CHILL TO THE SUNLESS AIR.

BUT OF ALL OF THESE SPIRITS, THERE IS ONE SPECTRE WHO SEEMS TO CONTROL ALL THEIR POWERS.

THE DOMINANT SPIRIT IS A FIGURE ON HORSEBACK, CLAD IN BLACK, AND *WITHOUT A HEAD!*

THUD!

THUD!

HE HAS OFTEN BEEN SEEN BY MANY OF THE LOCALS, IN AND AROUND THE VILLAGE AND ITS NEIGHBOURING ROADS, AND THIS GHOST WHO RIDES LIKE A MIDNIGHT BLAST IS KNOWN BY ALL AS *THE HEADLESS HORSEMAN OF SLEEPY HOLLOW.*

BUT PERHAPS, DEAR READER, THIS STORY WOULD NOT BE TOLD AT ALL IF IT WERE NOT FOR THE ARRIVAL OF THE NEW SCHOOLMASTER, *ICHABOD CRANE.*

A TALL AND LANKY, ALMOST GOOFY LOOKING FELLOW.

WITH NARROW SHOULDERS, AND ARMS THAT HUNG A MILE PAST HIS SLEEVES...

HIS HEAD WAS SMALL AND FLAT. HE HAD EARS LIKE AN ELEPHANT'S, LARGE GREEN EYES AND A LONG NOSE. HE LOOKED LIKE A WEATHERVANE POINTING THE DIRECTION OF THE WIND.

THE SCHOOLHOUSE WAS A SIMPLE, ONE-ROOM LOG BUILDING NEXT TO A CREEK. ICHABOD BROUGHT HIS OWN SENSE OF HOW HE WOULD 'ENLIGHTEN' THE YOUTH OF WHAT HE CONSIDERED THESE 'SIMPLE-MINDED' COUNTRY FOLK.

AND ICHABOD WAS NOT THE NICEST TEACHER, GOODNESS NO! HE WAS QUITE STRICT, WITH A FIERCE ATTITUDE THE CHILDREN HAD NEVER EXPERIENCED BEFORE.

...AND FEET THAT LOOKED LIKE SHOVELS.

HE WOULD TAKE FULL ADVANTAGE OF THIS, ACTING AS A KING RULING OVER HIS SUBJECTS IN THAT CLASSROOM.

HE USUALLY STOOD NEXT TO THE *WHIPPING STICK*, WITH A HAND-SLAPPING RULER POISED LIKE AN EMPEROR'S SCEPTRE.

IT WAS A REMINDER TO THE CHILDREN WHAT *PAINS* WOULD BEFALL THEM IF THEY WERE CAUGHT NOT PAYING ATTENTION.

NOR DID IT PLEASE SOME OF THE SLIGHTLY POORER FAMILIES. FOR ALTHOUGH ICHABOD WAS A VERY SKINNY FELLOW, HE HAD THE *APPETITE OF A PIG!*

AND EATING WAS ONE OF ICHABOD'S FAVOURITE PASTIMES.

OUTSIDE THE CLASSROOM, ICHABOD CRANE WOULD WEAR A VERY DIFFERENT FACE. HE DID NOT EARN MUCH MONEY. IT WAS CUSTOM FOR THE TEACHER TO STAY WITH HIS STUDENTS' FAMILIES IN ROTATION FOR A WEEK AT A TIME.

THIS DID NOT PLEASE THE STUDENTS AT ALL!

BUT THERE WERE MORE CURIOUS THINGS TO THIS MAN WHO CLAIMED TO BE OF A 'HIGHER INTELLIGENCE'.

FOR JUST LIKE THOSE NATIVES OF THE HOLLOW, ICHABOD WAS A VERY SUPERSTITIOUS FELLOW.

ICHABOD HAD READ SEVERAL BOOKS THOROUGHLY. BUT THE ONE THAT CAPTURED HIS INTEREST THE MOST WAS HIS COPY OF THE HISTORY OF NEW ENGLAND WITCHCRAFT. AND WITCHCRAFT WAS ONE OF THE MANY THINGS ICHABOD FIRMLY BELIEVED IN.

LA-LA!

LA-LA!

LA-LA!

AWOOO!

AMONG HIS OTHER PASTIMES, ICHABOD FANCIED HIMSELF AS A SINGER. HE TOOK IT UPON HIMSELF TO GIVE THE LADIES CHOIR LESSONS IN SINGING THE CHURCH HYMNS.

EVEN THOUGH IT WAS JOKED BEHIND HIS BACK THAT ICHABOD'S OWN SINGING RESEMBLED THE HOWLING OF A DOG!

BUT AS ICHABOD WAS CONSIDERED AN EDUCATED GENTLEMAN, HE WAS NOT WHAT THE WOMEN OF SLEEPY HOLLOW WERE USED TO. SOON, HE BECAME A RATHER WELCOME FIGURE IN FEMALE SOCIAL CIRCLES.

AND MANY OF ICHABOD'S NIGHTS WERE SPENT WITH THE LADIES TELLING ALL MANNER OF *GHOST STORIES*. THE OLD WIVES DELIGHTED IN TALKING ABOUT THE LOCAL HAUNTS, AND ICHABOD, IN TURN, WOULD *TEASE* AND *FRIGHTEN* THEM WITH STORIES OF WITCHCRAFT FROM HIS BOOK.

HEE HEE HEE!

HA-HA!

HA-HA!

OOOH!

READ THE REST OF THIS STORY IN: THE LEGEND OF SLEEPY HOLLOW